LATIGO

BY STAN LYNDE

BOOK TWO: 1980-1981

Introductions by Stan Lynde

Layouts by Joe Ferreira

COTTONWOOD GRAPHICS, INC.

2340 Trumble Creek Road
Kalispell, Montana 59901-6713

LATIGO, BOOK ONE: 1980-1981

Published by Cottonwood Graphics, Inc.
2340 Trumble Creek Road
Kalispell, Montana 59901-6713

Cottonwood Graphics, Inc., 2340 Trumble Creek Road, Kalispell, MT 59901-6713

Printed in the U.S.A.

135798642

Library of Congress Catalog Card Number: 91-77330

ISBN: 0-9626999-7-7

First Printing November 1992

To Rob a Bank

July of 1980 found me well into my second year with Cole "Latigo" Cantrell, and his adventures in the Montana Territory of the 1870s and 80s.

Unlike the previous year, 1979, when both my first syndicated strip, *Rick O'Shay*, and my second, *Latigo*, ran in newspapers across the country at the same time, *Latigo* had now become virtually the only western story strip in print. Story strips in general were in a state of decline, as space allotted strips by editors grew ever smaller and as the impact of television and the VCR was perceived to grow ever greater.

The prevailing wisdom in the industry said that readers were no longer willing to wait ten to thirteen weeks to see how a comic strip story would unfold when they could watch a movie on television in an evening, or an entire mini-series in two or three. The only trouble with the prevailing wisdom was that, as usual, it was wrong. Besides making the mistake of comparing apples to oranges --measuring the popularity of comics against their cousin film--those who made the comparison underestimated the loyalty of comics readers, who continued to faithfully follow their favorite strips, whether gag-a-day or story, and--presumably--also watch television movies and mini-series. At any rate, *Latigo* continued to hold, and add to, its list of client newspapers.

The strip's second year began on July 7 with the tale of sodbuster Simms and his short but eventful life of crime in a story I call **To Rob a Bank.**

U.S. Marshal Hoodoo Hawks and the pompous and wrong-headed commandant of Fort Savage, Major Fairweather, make their initial appearances in this story.

Meanwhile, in the town of Whiplash, banker Flint Skinner has troubles of his own..

THE BANK EXAMINER IS COMING,, NEXT WEEK! WHAT AM I GOING TO DO?

WHEN I BORROWED THAT MONEY FROM THE BANK'S ACCOUNTS, I WAS SO CERTAIN I COULD REPAY IT!

AH,, WHAT A DARK DAY, RAIN AND DRIZZLE,, WHEN FIRST WE PRACTICE TO EMBEZZLE.

THOSE INVESTMENTS SEEMED SO SURE,,AND I KEPT BORROWING MORE AND MORE OF MY DEPOSITORS' MONEY,,

,,MORE THAN EIGHT THOUSAND DOLLARS OF IT! ALL GONE,,LOST! AND NOW THE BANK EXAMINER'S COMING!

BUT I MUSTN'T PANIC,, I MUST MAINTAIN AN ATTITUDE OF CALM AND CONFIDENCE,,

IT ALWAYS FRIGHTENS DEPOSITORS TO SEE THEIR BANKER CRY.

IT ALL BEGAN SO WELL,, I FOUNDED THIS BANK,, I WORKED HARD, AND I PROSPERED!

I MADE PEOPLE TRUST ME! I SMILED! I SHOOK HANDS! I GAVE AWAY PENS AND CALENDARS!

AND MY ACCOUNTS GREW, AS DID MY INCOME. AND ALWAYS, I WORRIED,, ABOUT FIRE, ABOUT COMPETITION, ABOUT OUTLAWS ROBBING ME,,

OH, WHERE ARE THE BANK ROBBERS NOW THAT I NEED THEM!

GRANGERS BANK of WHIPLASH

LOOKS LIKE WE'RE A MITE LATE, MULE,,THE BANK'S ALREADY CLOSED FOR THE DAY,,

,,BUT I RECKON BANKER SKINNER'S STILL THERE, COUNTIN' MONEY, FORECLOSURES, AN' SUCH,,

OH! IT'S YOU, SIMMS. I WAS HOPING,,ER, AFRAID,, YOU MIGHT BE A THIEF!

YOU MEAN YOU WON'T PURSUE THOSE **BANDITS**? YOU CERTAINLY ARE A POOR EXCUSE FOR A **PEACE** OFFICER, BUCK!

WHAT'D YOU **EXPECT** FOR TEN DOLLARS A MONTH,, **WILD BILL HICKOK**?

ANYWAYS, I GOT NO **AUTHORITY** T' GO CHASIN' BANK ROBBERS ALL OVER **INJUN** COUNTRY,,

,,SO IF YOU WANT 'EM **PURSUED**, YOU'LL HAVE T' TELEGRAPH THE **U.S. MARSHAL** IN CAPITAL CITY,,

ON THE OTHER HAND, IF YOU **DON'T** WANT 'EM PURSUED, I'M YOUR **MAN**!

STAN LYNDE

CAPITAL CITY..

STAN LYNDE

TELEGRAM FOR YOU, HOODOO, FROM OVER **WHIPLASH** WAY.

WHIPLASH, HUH?

READ 'ER TO ME, BEAUREGARD,, I CAN'T FIND MY **READIN'** GLASSES.

YOU CAN'T FIND 'EM 'CAUSE YOU DON'T **HAVE** ANY, HOODOO,,

,,AND IF YOU **DID** HAVE 'EM, YOU **STILL** COULDN'T READ 'CAUSE EVER'BODY KNOWS YOU CAN'T READ WORTH **DIDDLY-SQUAT**!

I CAN **SHOOT**, THOUGH,, *READ* 'ER TO ME, BEAUREGARD.

KLATCH!

SO,, OUTLAWS HIT THE WHIPLASH BANK AN RODE SOUTH INTO **INJUN** COUNTRY, DID THEY?

HOODOO HAWKS, US MARSHAL

WANTED DEAD OR ALIVE "KID" KIRALLY

STAN LYNDE

MIGHT BE THE **SNIPES** GANG,, THEY'VE BEEN **SEEN** LATELY IN THAT AREA,,

,,THEY AIN'T ANY O' THEM BOYS SMART ENOUGH T' POUR SAND OUT OF A **BOOT**,,

,,BUT THEN IT DON'T **REQUIRE** MUCH BRAINS T' HOLD UP A BANK.

MISTER SKINNER? I'M **HOODOO HAWKS**, U.S. MARSHAL. I GOT YOUR **TELEGRAM**.

MARSHAL HAWKS! THANK HEAVEN YOU'RE **HERE**!

GRANGERS BANK — FLINT SKINNER, PRESIDENT

OUTLAWS ROBBED THE BANK LAST WEEK,, THEY GOT AWAY WITH OVER **TEN THOUSAND DOLLARS**!

UH-HUH. HOW MANY OF 'EM **WAS** THEY?

AT LEAST **SIX**,, MAYBE **SEVEN**! I'M NOT **SURE**, EXACTLY,,

NEITHER AM *I*,,

,,BUT CUTTIN' THE NUMBERS BY **HALF**, I FIGURE THREE MEN OR LESS MEBBE TOOK YOU FOR **FIVE THOUSAND**.

STAN LYNDE

ALL RIGHT, MARSHAL,,I'LL HELP YOU TRACK DOWN YOUR BANK ROBBERS. HOW MANY WERE THERE?

WELL, NOW,,THERE IS SOME QUESTION ABOUT THAT,,

,,BANKER SKINNER SAYS SIX OR SEVEN, SO I FIGURE MAYBE THREE OR FOUR,,

,,EXCEPT THAT NOBODY ELSE IN TOWN SAW THEM, AND WE DON'T KNOW FOR SURE WHICH WAY THEY WENT.

AND THIS ROBBERY HAPPENED A WEEK AGO?

YEP. BUT OTHER'N THAT, OUR JOB SHOULD BE FAIRLY EASY.

THERE'S A TRADIN' POST IN THE GAP BETWEEN THOSE TWO MOUNTAIN RANGES, MARSHAL,,

,,AND IF THOSE BANK ROBBERS RODE SOUTH INTO CROW COUNTRY, THEY MAY HAVE STOPPED THERE.

COULD BE,,RECKON IT'S WORTH LOOKIN' INTO, ANYWAY.

I'VE ALLUS FOUND THE BEST WAY TO HUNT OUTLAWS IS TO FIND A STARTIN' PLACE.

I'M HOODOO HAWKS, FRIEND,,AND I'M HUNTIN' SOME FELLERS. I FIGURE YOU MIGHT'VE SEEN 'EM.

MEBBE,,BUT WHY WOULD I TELL YOU?

GOOD QUESTION. I'VE GOT CASH MONEY AND A MEAN DISPOSITION,, I'M WILLIN' T' USE WHICHEVER WORKS.

SO NOW I GUESS YOU HAVE T' DECIDE WHETHER YOU PREFER PROFIT OR PAIN.

THERE WAS A FELLER CAME THROUGH HERE ABOUT THE TIME YOU'RE TALKIN' ABOUT, BUT HE WAS ALONE.

SAD LOOKIN' BIRD, HE WAS,,RIDIN' AN OLD MULE AN' CARRYIN' A CARPETBAG. HE BOUGHT SOME NEEDFULS FROM ME,,

,,AN' PAID FOR IT WITH THIS HERE NEW BANK NOTE. BUT HE SURE DIDN'T LOOK LIKE NO OUTLAW.

MAYBE NOT,,

,,BUT THIS HERE GREENBACK TELLS ANOTHER STORY.

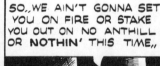

NOW ACCORDIN' TO BANKER SKINNER, SOME SIX OR SEVEN MEN ROBBED HIS BANK,,

,,AND MADE OFF WITH OVER TEN THOUSAND DOLLARS. SEEMS LIKE YOUR STORY IS SOME DIFFERENT.

ONLY IN DETAILS, MARSHAL,,

,,SUCH AS I DONE IT ALONE, AN' THE TOTAL TAKE WAS ONLY A HUNNERT AN' SIXTY-ONE DOLLARS!

STAN LYNDE

NOW LET ME GET THIS STRAIGHT, SIMMS, YOU SAY YOU ROBBED THE WHIPLASH BANK ALL BY YOUR LONESOME,,

,,AN' RODE OFF ON YOUR OLD MULE,, BY DAYLIGHT,, WITH A HUNDRED AND SIXTY-ONE DOLLARS.

BUT THEN THE SNIPES GANG TOOK THE MONEY AND YOUR MULE, AND SHOT YOU! IS THAT ABOUT IT?

YEAH. SORTER WILD, AIN'T IT?

STAN LYNDE

SORTER,, BUT THE REALLY WILD PART IS I BELIEVE EVERY WORD OF IT!

WELL, SIMMS,, WE'RE GONNA LEAVE YOU HERE WHILE WE GO FIND THE SNIPES GANG,, AND THE BANK'S MONEY,,

,,BUT I'M GONNA EXPECT YOU T' BE A-SETTIN' IN THAT EXACT SAME SPOT WHEN WE COME BACK.

IF YOU AIN'T, AN' WE HAVE T' GO LOOKIN' FOR YOU, I JUST MIGHT COMMENCE T' GET IRRITATED.

STAN LYNDE

WELL, LATIGO? WHAT DO YOU THINK OF SIMMS' STORY?

I'M INCLINED TO BELIEVE IT, HOODOO,,

,,IF ONLY BECAUSE IT'S TOO CRAZY TO BE A LIE! BESIDES, HE STRIKES ME AS AN HONEST MAN.

UH-HUH. HE SURE DON'T SEEM LIKE NO BANK ROBBER,,

STAN LYNDE

,,AND IN SPITE OF HIS CONFESSION, I'M BEGINNIN' T' DOUBT THAT HE IS.

NOW THERE IS SOME DIFFER'NCE BETWEEN YOUR STORY OF THE ROBBERY AND WHAT MISTER SIMMS HERE TELLS ME,,

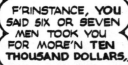

F'RINSTANCE, YOU SAID SIX OR SEVEN MEN TOOK YOU FOR MORE'N TEN THOUSAND DOLLARS,,

,,WHEREAS MISTER SIMMS CLAIMS HE DONE IT ALONE AN' GOT ONLY $161.00, WHICH AMOUNT WE RECOVERED.

HE ALSO SAYS YOU HELPED HIM ROB YOUR BANK,, AN' YOU KNOW SOMETHIN'? I BELIEVE HIM.

STAN LYNDE

I'VE SPENT MY LIFETIME A-LOOKIN' INTO THE EYES OF DES'PRIT MEN, BANKER SKINNER,,

,,AN' I'D BET MY NEW NAVVY-HO BLANKET THAT YOU, SIR, ARE AS DES'PRIT AS THEY COME.

I SEE GUILT IN YOUR LEFT EYE AN' FEAR IN YOUR RIGHT EYE,, AN' THERE'S ONLY ONE CURE FOR IT,,

,,'FESS UP, AN' TAKE YOUR MEDICINE.

STAN LYNDE

ALL,, ALL RIGHT,, YES, I LIED,, AND I DID HELP SIMMS ROB THE BANK.

THE BANK EXAMINER WAS COMING, AND I HAD A SHORTAGE IN MY ACCOUNTS.

STAN LYNDE

I'D BORROWED FROM THE ACCOUNTS, YOU SEE, TO MAKE CERTAIN INVESTMENTS,,

WHICH TURNED OUT TO BE UNCERTAIN INVESTMENTS.

WELL, SKINNER,, I'M AFRAID THE INTEREST IS DUE ON THAT MONEY YOU BORROWED.

STAN LYNDE

YOU,, YOU WON'T NEED THE HANDCUFFS, MARSHAL,, I'LL GO PEACEABLY. DO,, DO YOU THINK I'LL GO TO PRISON?

THAT'S UP TO THE JUDGE, MISTER SKINNER,,

,,I'M JUST AN OLD LAWDOG, AN' MY JOB IS FETCHIN' LAWBREAKERS, NOT JUDGIN' EM,,

,,BUT I DO THINK YOU MIGHT BE WISE T' CANCEL YOUR APPOINTMENTS FOR THE NEXT EIGHT OR TEN YEARS.

Vengeance Trail

From the beginning, *Latigo* was a true joint effort and a partnership between myself and Field Newspaper Syndicate. Field's then president, Dick Sherry, had contacted me in 1978 to request that I create a new western strip for Field, and he supported my efforts from the start with a strong promotional and marketing effort.

Among the ancillary projects Dick initiated were a series of text paperback novels through Fawcett Popular Library--four titles in the series were published--and a planned comic book series beginning with *Latigo's* origin story in two full-color books to be published in the United Kingdom.

I was to write the books, of course, but the demanding schedule necessary to produce the daily strip itself would make it impossible for me to draw them. Both Dick and I wanted the best artist we could find to draw the books, and I'm convinced we found that person in Russ Heath.

A thorough professional, Russ brought an authentic and compatible style to the work, and he not only adapted the principal characters I had drawn previously, he created with skill and care the appearances of characters I had not drawn, including *Latigo's* parents and the four killers.

I've never known exactly what happened, but that first comic book, written and colored by me and drawn by Russ, never saw publication. It was adapted, however, in 1980 and 1981, to tell the origin story of *Latigo* in the daily newspaper strip, and the result was a blend of Russ' and my art.

I've always regretted that the comic book never saw print; certainly Russ Heath's excellent work has suffered by being forced into the restricted format of the daily newspaper strip. It simply wasn't produced with that end in mind. I do believe, however, that Russ Heath fans and devotees of good western art in general will find **Vengeance Trail** worth their time.

TO THE READER:

WE PAUSE BRIEFLY IN THE CONTINUING ADVENTURES OF COLE "LATIGO" CANTRELL TO CONSIDER SOME OF THE QUESTIONS YOU HAVE ASKED ABOUT HIM.

WHO *IS* LATIGO? WHAT WERE HIS ORIGINS? WHAT WERE THE FORCES WHICH SHAPED HIS LIFE AND CHARACTER?

THE FOLLOWING STORY, WHICH BEGINS TOMORROW IN THIS NEWSPAPER, PROVIDES SOME OF THE ANSWERS.

STAN LYNDE

© Field Enterprises, Inc., 1980

9/30

APRIL, 1865 -- AND THIS YEAR, AFTER FOUR LONG, BLOODY YEARS OF THAT NATIONAL AGONY CALLED CIVIL WAR, THE SEASON OF SPRING BRINGS -- FINALLY -- THE PROMISE OF LIFE, AND PEACE,,,

,,,BUT THE PROMISE IS NOT YET FACT,,,

© Field Enterprises, Inc., 1980

STAN LYNDE *and* RUSS HEATH

10/1

IF YOU KNOW ANY PRAYERS, REB, YOU'D BEST SAY ONE,, YOU'VE GOT ABOUT FIVE SECONDS T' LIVE!

AH HAVE NOTHIN' AGAINST THE **ALMIGHTY**, IF SUCH THERE BE,,

© Field Enterprises, Inc., 1980

BUT AH'D FIND IT **TEDIOUS** PRAYIN' TO A DEITY WHO CREATED YANKEE SCUM LIKE YOU.

SUIT YOURSELF, REB,,

HOLD IT, SERGEANT!

10/2

NOW WHAT'S GOIN' ON HERE, SERGEANT,, WHO *IS* THAT MAN?

A PRISONER, CAP'N,, ONE O' MOSBY'S MURDERIN' DEVILS,,

,,WE CAPTURED HIM THIS MORNIN', SIR,, AND WE WERE ABOUT TO MAKE A GOOD REBEL OUT OF HIM.

WE DON'T **EXECUTE** PRISONERS IN **MY** COMMAND, SOLDIER,, NOT EVEN **MOSBY'S** MEN,,

© Field Enterprises, Inc., 1980

,,AND, AS A PERSONAL **FAVOR**, I'LL FORGET THAT YOU **INTENDED** TO.

AH'M GRATEFUL FOR YOUR TIMELY **ARRIVAL**, CAPTAIN,, AH HAD NO REAL **WISH** TO BE HANGED.

AN UNDERSTANDABLE **RELUCTANCE**, LIEUTENANT. **DID** YOU SERVE WITH MOSBY?

AH HAD THAT HONOR, SUH. AH AM LIEUTENANT **GAYLORD SATEEN**, OF MOSBY'S IRREGULARS. YOUR **PRISONER**, SUH.

YOU'RE A LUCKY **MAN**, LIEUTENANT. I GUESS YOU KNOW FEELINGS AGAINST MOSBY'S RAIDERS RUN **HIGH** HERE IN SIXTH CORPS.

AH DO UNDERSTAND, SUH,, WE HAVE BEEN **TROUBLESOME**, HAVE WE NOT?

BUT AH HOLD NO ILL FEELIN'S. YANKEE BLUEBELLIES ARE MERELY MEN, AFTER ALL,,

,,AN' MANKIND MUST **SURELY** BE ONE O' THE ALMIGHTY'S GREATEST FAILURES.

YOUR CAPTAIN SAVED MAH **LIFE**, CORPORAL,, AH AM IN HIS **DEBT.** MIGHT AH ASK HIS **NAME**?

'DON'T **SEE** WHY **NOT**, REB,,

,,THAT'S CAP'N **COLE CANTRELL**,, HALF IRISH, HALF INDIAN, AN' ALL MAN. HE'S ONE O' THE BEST DANG OFFICERS PHIL SHERIDAN **HAS**,,

,,AN' IT'S BECAUSE O' MEN LIKE **HIM** THAT YOU REBS ARE **LOSIN'** THIS WAR.

THAT MAY **BE**, CORPORAL,,

,,BUT AH BELIEVE THAT YOUR HAVIN' MORE MEN, MONEY, AN' **SUPPLIES** IS BY FAR THE **GREATER** FACTOR.

CAPTAIN CANTRELL REPORTING AS ORDERED, GENERAL,, YOU SENT FOR ME, SIR?

YES, CAPTAIN,, I DID. SIT DOWN, PLEASE.

THE DAY WE'VE ALL LOOKED FORWARD TO HAS COME AT **LAST**, COLE,, GENERAL LEE **SURRENDERED** THIS MORNING AT APPOMATTOX COURT HOUSE.

THE JOB IS FINISHED, COLE,, AND THE UNION IS **PRESERVED.** TO THE **UNION!**

YES,,

,,AND TO THOSE WHO **DIED** TO PRESERVE IT.

WELL, LACKMAN,,WHAT IS THE STATUS OF OUR NORTHERN ROUTE?

IT IS PROCEEDING, MR. MAX,,

NEW YORK CITY...

IT IS PROCEEDING TOO SLOWLY, LACKMAN! WE MUST ACQUIRE THE RIGHT OF WAY AND BEGIN LAYING TRACK!

YES, SIR,, AND WE ARE DOING SO, BUT,,

,,THERE ARE SOME SETTLERS IN THE AREA WHO REFUSE TO SELL, AND,,

REFUSE? REFUSE TO SELL?

I DO NOT ACCEPT SUCH OBSTACLES LACKMAN,, ELIMINATE THEM!

BUT, MR. MAX,,THE SETTLERS HAVE VALID CLAIMS TO THEIR LAND! WE ARE NEGOTIATING,,

I SAID ELIMINATE THEM, LACKMAN,, REMOVE THEM FROM THE PATH OF PROGRESS!

BUT MR. MAX,, LEGALLY, WE CAN'T,,

LEGALLY!!

THE CAESARS DID NOT PERMIT LEGALITY TO IMPEDE THE PROGRESS OF THEIR EMPIRE,,THEY WERE THE LAW! AND SO, LACKMAN, AM I!

SEND MY CENTURIONS AND GLADIATORS FORTH AGAINST THOSE VERMIN,,I WANT THEM DESTROYED!

BEAVER VALLEY,, AT THE FOOTHILLS OF THE ROCKIES,,

YOUR EYES WILL GROW TIRED FROM SO MUCH LOOKING, WOMAN. OUR SON WILL COME BACK SOON.

YES, MY HUSBAND,,

,,THE WHITE MAN'S WAR IS OVER, AND COLE HAS BECOME A GREAT WARRIOR. BUT HE WILL ALWAYS BE MY LITTLE ONE.

I KNOW,, AND I THANK GOD FOR SPARIN' HIM. I'M GLAD HE'S COMIN' HOME.

THOSE RAILROAD MEN WANT OUR LAND, WHITE ELK,,AN' THEY WON'T QUIT UNTIL THEY GET IT. THIS CHILD SMELLS TROUBLE.

WE WILL FIGHT THEM IF WE MUST, MY HUSBAND.

WE SURELY WILL, WOMAN,, BUT I WOULDN'T MIND HAVIN' COLE'S HELP.

RIDERS COME, HUSBAND.

MOTHER... DAD!

FOUR LONG YEARS OF KILLING,, I REALLY THOUGHT ALL THAT WAS BEHIND ME FOR GOOD,,UNTIL **NOW**.

FOUR MEN,, **WHITE** MEN. THEY TRIED **HARD** TO MAKE THIS LOOK LIKE AN **INDIAN** RAID,,

,,AND THEY RODE DUE **WEST**. IN NO PARTICULAR **HURRY**,, GUESS THEY DIDN'T **FIGURE** ON BEING **FOLLOWED**,,

,,BUT THEY **WILL** BE.

BECAUSE THOSE KILLERS ARE WHITE MEN, THEY'LL BE HEADING FOR A **TOWN**,, A PLACE WHERE THERE'S **WHISKEY** AND **WOMEN**.

NEAREST TOWN **WEST** WOULD BE **SCALPLOCK**, AND THAT'S SIXTY MILES **AWAY**,, SO THERE'S TIME,,

,,TIME TO TAKE MOTHER BACK TO HER PEOPLE, THE **CROW**. AND THEN, TROOPER, **WE** TAKE THE **WAR** TRAIL.

10/27

HOLD, LONG KNIFE SOLDIER! WHAT DO YOU SEEK AMONG THE LODGES OF THE CROW?

MY MOTHER WAS WHITE ELK, AND THE CROW ARE HER PEOPLE. SHE SHOULD REST AMONG THEM.

I AM HER SON, AND THE SON OF THE FUR TRAPPER "BADGER" CANTRELL. YOUR PEOPLE CALL ME "TWO TRAILS."

I HAVE HEARD OF THESE PEOPLE, TWO TRAILS,, AND OF YOU. COME,, YOU ARE WELCOME! KAHAY!

10/28

HIGH ABOVE THE CROW CAMP, COLE "BURIES" HIS PARENTS IN THE MANNER OF HIS MOTHER'S PEOPLE AND GRIEVES, SILENTLY AND ALONE.

10/29

WELL,, IT'S FINISHED,, THERE'S NOTHING MORE I CAN DO HERE,,

IT IS YOU, TWO TRAILS. I HAD A MEDICINE DREAM THAT YOU WOULD COME.

10/30

MY HEART IS ON THE GROUND FOR YOUR SORROW, TALL ONE.

A-HO', DARK STAR,, THANK YOU.

YOU HAVE GROWN BEAUTIFUL SINCE OUR CHILDHOOD. YOUR HUSBAND MUST BE PROUD.

I HAVE NO HUSBAND, TWO TRAILS,, I AM A MEDICINE WOMAN.

COLE RIDES THE HIGH PLAINS WEST, SEEKING THE MEN WHO KILLED HIS PARENTS,,

,,AND THEN, JUST BEFORE NOON, HIS SEARCH IS REWARDED,, HE CUTS THEIR TRAIL!

THOSE KILLERS ARE MIGHTY CARELESS,,THEY'RE MOVIN' SLOW, LEAVIN' TRACKS A RIBBON-CLERK COULD FOLLOW.

FOUR MEN, ON TIRED HORSES,,ONE WITH A SPLIT HOOF. JUST AHEAD, SOMEPLACE, THEY MUST HAVE MADE CAMP LAST NIGHT.

YEP,,THEY CAMPED HERE, AND SLEPT LATE. ASHES ARE STILL WARM,,

,,WHICH MEANS I CAN CATCH UP TO 'EM BY SUNDOWN IF THESE CROW BUFFALO PONIES ARE AS TOUGH AS THEY SEEM.

TIME TO SWITCH HORSES AND DO SOME HARD RIDIN',,THOSE BOYS SURE AREN'T WATCHIN' THEIR BACK-TRAIL,,

,,AND UNLESS THEY CHANGE THEIR WAYS, THAT JUST MIGHT BE A FATAL MISTAKE.

HOW MUCH FARTHER YOU FIGGER IT IS TO SCALPLOCK, STARK? SEEMS I CAN SMELL THE WHISKEY FROM HERE!

IF YOU CAN, YOUR NOSE WORKS BETTER'N YOUR BRAIN, CUTTER,,

,,I'D GUESS IT T' BE ABOUT TEN MORE MILE,,HEY!

THERE'S A RIDER BEHIND US, LEADIN' A HORSE! HE JUST DROPPED BEHIND THAT FAR RIDGE.

A RIDER? INJUN OR WHITE MAN?

TOO FAR T' TELL FOR SURE,, LOOKED LIKE INJUN HORSES, ALL RIGHT,,

CHANCES ARE, HE AIN'T FOLLERIN' US,,BUT I RECKON HE'LL BEAR WATCHIN'.

31.

NO SIGN O' LEWT,, MEBBE HE GOT THAT RIDER, AN' MEBBE HE **DIDN'T**. I FIGGER WE ORTER SPLIT **UP**.

© Field Enterprises, Inc., 1980

YOU BOYS DO WHATEVER YOU'VE A **MIND** TO, BUT I'M RIDIN' SOUTH T' BASIN CITY.

I CAN STILL SMELL THAT WHISKEY YONDER IN **SCALPLOCK**, STARK,,

,,RECKON I'LL RIDE IN AN' GET ME SOME. HOW 'BOUT YOU, DAIN?

STARK'S RIGHT,, WE SHOULD SPLIT UP.

THERE'S A MININ' CAMP MEBBE TEN MILES **NORTH** O' HERE CALLED **NEW SODOM**,,

,,IT AIN'T AS CLOSE AS SCALPLOCK, BUT THEN I AIN'T AS THIRSTY AS YOU, CUTTER.

ALL RIGHT,, WE'LL MEET TWO WEEKS FROM NOW IN BASIN CITY. STAY LOOSE, BOYS.

© Field Enterprises, Inc., 1980

SO,, THEY'VE SPLIT UP. WELL, THAT JUST MEANS IT'S GOING TO BE ONE AT A **TIME**.

AS DUSK FALLS OVER SCALPLOCK, COLE RIDES SLOWLY UP THE MUDDY, RUTTED STREET,,

© Field Enterprises, Inc., 1980

,,CAREFULLY, HE STUDIES THE HORSES AT THE HITCHRACKS, SEARCHING,, UNTIL HE FINDS WHAT HE'S BEEN LOOKING FOR,,

IN SCALPLOCK, COLE DISMOUNTS, AND LIFTS THE HOOF OF THE LATHERED ROAN AT THE HITCHRACK.

THERE IT IS,, THAT SPLIT REAR HOOF I'VE BEEN TRACKIN' SO MANY MILES,,

,,AND NOW, HORSE, YOU'RE GONNA HELP **ME**,,

© Field Enterprises, Inc., 1980

WHAP!

IN NEW SODOM,,

DAIN! CHARLIE DAIN! I AIN'T SEEN YOU IN A DOG'S AGE!

HULLO, SAM,, DIDN'T THINK YOU'D REMEMBER ME.

I NEVER FORGET A BIG SPENDER, CHARLIE,, WHAT BRINGS YOU TO THIS HELL-HOLE?

WHISKEY RIGHT NOW, SAM,, THEN A WOMAN.

NEITHER ONE O' THEM ITEMS ARE MUCH TO BRAG ABOUT IN THIS CAMP,, I HOPE YOU AIN'T PARTICULAR.

© Field Enterprises, Inc., 1980

SAY, SAM,, COULD I HAVE A WORD WITH YOU?

SURE, ABNER. 'SCUSE ME, CHARLIE.

NAT FANNER, THE MARSHAL DOWN AT SCALPLOCK, WANTED ME T' ASK AROUND ABOUT A MAN,,

© Field Enterprises, Inc., 1980

,,TALL FELLER, DARK-HAIRED,, WEARS BUCK-SKINS AND RIDES AN INJUN PONY. CALLS HIMSELF COLE CANTRELL.

THIS FELLER CANTRELL KILLED A MAN NAMED CUTTER IN SCALPLOCK LAST NIGHT, THEN HEADED THIS WAY. YOU HAVEN'T SEEN HIM, HAVE YOU?

NO,, I AIN'T SEEN NOBODY LIKE THAT AROUND HERE,,

,,BUT IF I DO, I'LL SURE SEND WORD DOWN T' NAT. I ALWAYS LIKE T' KEEP IN GOOD WITH THE LAW.

SURE, YOU DO. THANKS, SAM.

© Field Enterprises, Inc., 1980

CUTTER,, DEAD! THAT FELLER WHO WAS FOLLOWIN' US KILLED HIM! HE MUST'VE GOT LEWT, TOO,, AN' NOW HE'S AFTER ME!

UH,, SAY, SAM,, IS THERE A ROOM UPSTAIRS WITH A GOOD VIEW OF THE STREET?

SURE, CHARLIE,, MY ROOM FRONTS ON THE STREET. WHY?

© Field Enterprises, Inc., 1980

IT'D BE WORTH, SAY, FIFTY DOLLARS TO ME IF I COULD USE YOUR ROOM,, AND THAT SHOTGUN YOU KEEP BEHIND THE BAR.

YOU GOT A DEAL, CHARLIE,,

,,AND I AIN'T ASKIN' ANY QUESTIONS 'CAUSE I DON'T WANT NO ANSWERS.

BASIN CITY,,

WELL? ANY TROUBLE?

NONE T' SPEAK OF,,

,,WE GUNNED OL' BADGER CANTRELL AN' HIS SQUAW SLICKER'N A DOG'S TOOTH. MADE IT LOOK LIKE THE CHEYENNE DONE IT,,

,,BUT THERE WAS SOMETHIN', A RIDER PICKED UP OUR TRAIL AN' FOLLERED US. I SENT LEWT BACK T' BUSHWHACK HIM.

AND?

AND,, I GUESS HE DONE IT. I RODE ON WITH CUTTER AN' DAIN, FAR AS SCALPLOCK,, AN' WE SPLIT UP.

STAN LYNDE

CUTTER STAYED AT SCALPLOCK, DAIN RODE ON T' NEW SODOM, AN' I CAME HERE T' COLLECT OUR PAY.

I SEE.

THE COMPANY DOESN'T PAY FOR BOTCHED JOBS, STARK,, SOMEBODY KNOWS YOU KILLED THOSE PEOPLE.

HUH?

WHAT D' YOU MEAN, BOTCHED? I TOLD YOU,, I SENT LEWT BACK T' GET THAT RIDER!

CORRECT PROCEDURE, STARK,,

,,BUT YOU SHOULD HAVE MADE SURE.

STAN LYNDE

,,THIS TELEGRAM CAME AN HOUR AGO FROM THE MARSHAL AT SCALPLOCK. CUTTER WAS KILLED IN A GUNFIGHT THERE NIGHT BEFORE LAST.

THE MARSHAL ALSO RECEIVED WORD FROM NEW SODOM THAT DAIN, TOO, HAS BEEN KILLED,, AND MY GUESS IS THAT LEWT IS DEAD, AS WELL.

INCIDENTALLY, THE MAN WHO KILLED CUTTER WORE BUCKSKINS AND RODE AN INDIAN PONY. HE TOLD THE MARSHAL HIS NAME WAS COLE CANTRELL!

CANTRELL!?

STAN LYNDE

THE COMPANY DOESN'T LIKE LOOSE ENDS, STARK,,

,,YOU'LL BE PAID, ALL RIGHT, BUT ONLY AFTER YOU'VE TAKEN CARE OF THAT RIDER. HE IS, NO DOUBT, ON HIS WAY HERE TO FIND YOU,,

STAN LYNDE

,,AND I SUGGEST THAT YOU MEET HIM ON THE WAY AND TIE UP THAT LOOSE END.

YEAH,, ALL RIGHT, CREED,, YOU'RE THE BOSS.

YES, STARK,, I CERTAINLY AM.

43.

Marshal of Rimfire

With the third and final story of *Latigo's* second year, our hero throws caution--and his Army career--to the winds in a confrontation with the arrogant Major Fairweather and finds himself in the guardhouse and facing serious charges. Once again, however, U.S. Marshal Hoodoo Hawks steps in (for reasons of his own) and Latigo becomes deputy U.S. Marshal under Hawks, and town marshal of Rimfire.

This story introduces cattle baron Rufus Cain and his son Buck in a story of strong men in opposition and strong wills in conflict. It also marks the return of cynical Duke Sateen and dancehall girl Aspen Groves, as Cole "Latigo" Cantrell faces a new test as **Marshal of Rimfire.**

GET TO YOUR FEET, COWBOY,, YOU'RE UNDER ARREST!

NOW, MARSHAL,,

STAN LYNDE

,,I RECKON YOU DIDN'T HEAR ME, SO I'LL MAKE IT PLAIN. THIS BOY IS ONE O' MY MEN,,

,,AN' THERE JUST AIN'T NO WAY YOU'RE GONNA TAKE HIM IN.

THIS IS A MATTER OF LAW, MR. CAIN,, I'M ARRESTIN' THAT COWBOY, AN' I'M ASKIN' YOU TO STAND ASIDE!

IT SOUNDS MORE LIKE YOU'RE TELLIN' ME TO,, AN' NO, I DON'T BELIEVE I WILL.

STAN LYNDE

THE WAY IT IS, MARSHAL,, IS THAT YOU'D BETTER BACK OFF, WHILE YOU STILL CAN.

YOU HEARD THE BOSS, LAWDOG,, YOU AIN'T TAKIN' THAT BOY TO JAIL,, BACK OFF!

BLAM!

STAN LYNDE

YOU,, YOU SHOT THE MARSHAL!

THAT'S RIGHT, DEPUTY,,

AN' YOU'RE NEXT, UNLESS YOU SHUCK THAT GUNBELT, RIGHT NOW!

KLATCH

STAN LYNDE

THAT'S A GOOD BOY. NOW IF YOU FIND YOURSELF A GOOD HORSE AN' LEAVE THIS TOWN REAL FAST,,

,,YOU JUST MIGHT LIVE T' SEE ANOTHER SUNRISE.

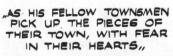

PLEASE UNDERSTAND ME, MR. CAMPBELL,, IT AIN'T THAT I DON'T SYMPATHIZE WITH YOUR PROBLEM, BECAUSE I DO,,

U.S. MARSHAL HOODOO HAWKS

,,BUT THIS IS A BIG TERRITORY, AND I JUST DON'T HAVE ENOUGH DEPUTIES TO COVER IT.

STAN LYNDE

HOWEVER,, THERE IS A MAN WHO MIGHT BE ABLE TO HELP YOU,,

HE AIN'T A LAWMAN RIGHT NOW, BUT HE SHOULD BE.

FORT SAVAGE,,

HEADQUARTER

BEGGIN' THE MAJOR'S PARDON, SIR,, BUT WE LOST FIVE HORSES LAST NIGHT,, INJUNS TOOK 'EM!

INDIANS ?

C.O.

YESSIR,, CROWS, THEY WAS,, TWO OF 'EM! CORPORAL MAYHEW FIRED AT 'EM,, BUT THEY GOT AWAY!

I SEE.

MONTANA TERRITO

© Field Enterprises, Inc., 1981

GO TELL CANTRELL I WANT TO SEE HIM, SERGEANT,, ON THE DOUBLE!

STAN LYNDE

THOSE TWO CROW INDIANS STOLE FIVE OF OUR HORSES LAST NIGHT, CANTRELL,, I WANT THEM BACK!

MONTANA TERRITORY

AND I WANT THOSE INDIANS BROUGHT BACK TOO,, DEAD OR ALIVE!

EASY, MAJOR,, IT'S AN INDIAN'S NATURE TO TAKE A HORSE NOW AND THEN.

CHANCES ARE SOME YOUNG HOT-BLOODS JUST GOT A LITTLE CARRIED AWAY.

I APPRECIATE YOUR KNOWLEDGE, ALTHOUGH I QUESTION YOUR TOLERANCE, CANTRELL,,

© Field Enterprises, Inc., 1981

,,BUT IN POINT OF FACT IT WAS OUR HORSES THAT WERE CARRIED AWAY, AND I WANT THEM BACK!

STAN LYNDE

YOU ARE TO RECOVER THOSE STOLEN ARMY HORSES, CANTRELL, AND THE INDIANS WHO TOOK THEM,, THAT'S AN ORDER!

I HEAR YOU, MAJOR,,

U.S.

THE CROW ARE IN THEIR BIG CAMP ON THE YELLOWSTONE RIGHT NOW, AND THEY'RE FRIENDLY TO THE ARMY.

I FIGURE THEY'LL RETURN THE HORSES WITHOUT ANY TROUBLE.

THEY HAD BETTER, MR. CANTRELL,,

© Field Enterprises, Inc., 1981

,,OR THE ARMY WILL BE IN THEIR BIG CAMP ON THE YELLOWSTONE!

STAN LYNDE

LOCK THAT MAN UP, SERGEANT,, UNDER HEAVY GUARD! I INTEND TO SEE HIM PROSECUTED TO THE MAXIMUM!

YES, SIR!

AND SEND A PATROL OUT AFTER THOSE INDIANS! I WANT THEM IN MY CUSTODY BY NIGHTFALL!

BEGGIN' THE MAJOR'S PARDON, SIR,,

,,BUT THOSE YOUNG BUCKS ARE LIKELY TO BE HALF WAY T' CANADA BY NOW,, WE'LL NEVER CATCH 'EM, SIR!

CAN'T ANYONE HERE OBEY A LAWFUL ORDER? DO AS I SAY, MULDOON!

TELL "A" TROOP TO GET MOUNTED, CORPORAL,, AND DRAW RATIONS FOR A THREE-DAY WILD GOOSE CHASE.

© Field Enterprises, Inc. 1981

STAN LYNDE

WELL, LADDY BUCK,, YOU'VE DONE IT THIS TIME, SURE AS THERE'S WHISKEY IN IRELAND.

I HAVE NO REGRETS, MULDOON.

GUARD HOUSE

AH, THAT WAS A FINE, LUSTY BLOW YOU STRUCK THE MAJOR, ALL RIGHT,, ALTHOUGH IT MAY PROVE A COSTLY ONE,,

,,BUT FOR WHAT IT'S WORTH, LATIGO, YOU'RE A HERO TO EVERY MAN ON THE POST.

© Field Enterprises, Inc. 1981

STAN LYNDE

OPEN THAT FOOL GATE, SOL'JER BOY,, THIS HERE'S U.S. MARSHAL HOODOO HAWKS TALKIN'!

FORT SAVAGE

MUCH OBLIGED, SONNY BOY,, KEEP AN EYEBALL ON MY OL' HORSE, WILL YOU?

AN' TREAT HIM GOOD, KID,, HE'S A CIVILIAN.

© Field Enterprises, Inc. 1981

STAN LYNDE

MORNIN', FAIRWEATHER! HOW'S YOUR OLD,, JUMPIN' JEZEBEL! WHO HIT YOU?

YOUR FRIEND DID, HAWKS,, CHIEF OF SCOUTS COLE "LATIGO" CANTRELL!

C.O.

AND I INTEND TO SEE HIM BREAKING ROCKS IN FEDERAL PRISON FOR THE REST OF HIS LIFE!

YOU SURE DO CARRY A MEAN GRUDGE, FAIRWEATHER,,

,,AN' I DO HATE T' DISAPPOINT YOU, BUT THE FACT IS I NEED HIM.

© Field Enterprises, Inc. 1981

STAN LYNDE

SO THIS IS RIMFIRE,, MY NEW HOME. NOT A BAD-LOOKIN' TOWN, AS TOWNS GO,,

,,BUT I'M NOT ALTOGETHER SURE OF WHAT I'M DOIN' HERE. I'VE NEVER LIKED TOWNS MUCH,,

,,AND NOW I'VE SIGNED ON TO BE MARSHAL OF THIS ONE! A MAN'S TRAIL SURE TAKES SOME STRANGE TURNS.

STAN LYNDE

MAYOR CAMPBELL? I'M COLE CANTRELL,, MARSHAL HAWKS SENT ME.

SO YOU'RE THE MAN CALLED LATIGO,, WELCOME! COME IN!

I'M SURE MARSHAL HAWKS FILLED YOU IN ON OUR PROBLEMS HERE IN RIMFIRE,,

SOME,, BUT I'D LIKE TO HEAR ABOUT THEM FROM YOU, MAYOR.

FAIR ENOUGH. SIT DOWN, PLEASE,, I CAN OFFER YOU EITHER GOOD COFFEE OR BAD WHISKEY!

STAN LYNDE

THIS IS A GOOD TOWN, COLE,, A TOWN WITH A FUTURE. IT BEGAN AS A GOLD CAMP BACK IN '62,,

,,BUT BECAUSE IT'S ON THE RAILROAD IT WAS ABLE TO SURVIVE WHEN THE CLAIMS PLAYED OUT,,

,,AND RIMFIRE BECAME A COW TOWN. THAT HAS BEEN BOTH OUR BLESSING,, AND OUR CURSE.

STAN LYNDE

THIS TOWN SERVES AS A SHIPPING AND SUPPLY CENTER FOR TWO BIG RANCHES,, AND FOR THE AREA'S HOMESTEADERS,,

,,BUT ONE OF THOSE RANCHES, IN ADDITION TO BEING OUR MAJOR SOURCE OF INCOME, IS OUR MOST SERIOUS PROBLEM.

RUFUS CAIN, OWNER OF THE M CROSS, RECOGNIZES NO LAW BUT HIS OWN WILL.

STAN LYNDE

RUFUS CAIN SEEMS TO BELIEVE HE'S ABOVE THE LAW,,HIS MEN RIDE ROUGHSHOD OVER THIS TOWN.

DURING THE PAST YEAR, SEVERAL OF OUR CITIZENS HAVE BEEN KILLED OR INJURED BY M CROSS COWBOYS,,

,,BUT, MOST SERIOUS OF ALL, CAIN'S MEN HAVE KILLED OUR LAST THREE PEACE OFFICERS!

STAN LYNDE

© Field Enterprises, Inc. 1981

I HOPE I'VE GIVEN YOU A CLEAR PICTURE OF WHAT YOU'LL BE UP AGAINST AS MARSHAL HERE,,

,,TO BE FRANK, I WOULDN'T BLAME YOU IF YOU TURNED US DOWN, BUT WE DO NEED YOU.

I'LL STAY, MAYOR,,I'LL WEAR THE STAR, AND I'LL DO THE JOB,,

,,AND I CAN PROMISE YOU I'LL DO MY VERY BEST TO AVOID BEING KILLED.

STAN LYNDE

© Field Enterprises, Inc. 1981

WELCOME TO RIMFIRE, MARSHAL,,THIS IS YOUR OFFICE, AND THE JAIL,,

,,AND THERE'S A CABIN NEARBY WHERE YOU CAN HANG YOUR HAT. IS THERE ANYTHING ELSE YOU NEED?

I COULD USE SOME TOWN CLOTHES, MAYOR, AND A HAIRCUT,,

,,AND THEN I THINK I'LL GO OUT AND GET ACQUAINTED WITH MY TOWN.

STAN LYNDE

© Field Enterprises, Inc. 1981

LIVERY STABL.

THE NAME'S CANTRELL, FRIEND,,COLE CANTRELL. I'M THE NEW MARSHAL HERE IN RIMFIRE.

WELL,,I'M ORSON BUGGIE, AN' YOU'VE GOT MY SYMPATHY.

I'M OBLIGED, ORSON,,THIS BIG FELLER IS TROOPER. I'D LIKE YOU TO BOARD HIM HERE.

GIVE HIM THE BEST OF CARE,, AND KEEP HIM TRAVEL READY, DAY AND NIGHT,,AND WE'LL GET ALONG JUST FINE.

STAN LYNDE

© Field Enterprises, Inc. 1981

3/16

AND DID OUR GOOD MAYOR INFORM YOU OF THE SITUATION WHICH PERVADES HERE IN RIMFIRE?

PRETTY MUCH, DUKE,, ESPECIALLY AS IT REGARDS THE M CROSS.

FROM WHAT HE SAYS, RUFUS CAIN AND HIS COWBOYS FIGURE THEY OWN THIS TOWN.

QUITE TRUE, COLE,, AND THEY SEEM TO PARTICULARLY RESENT LAWMEN.

WELL,, I HAVEN'T BEEN A LAWMAN VERY LONG, BUT I PARTICULARLY RESENT LAWBREAKERS.

STAN LYNDE

© Field Enterprises, Inc. 1981

3/17

ONE WORD O' WARNIN', COLE,, AS TROUBLESOME AS RUFUS CAIN, HIS SONS, AN' HIS COWBOYS MIGHT BE,,

,,THERE IS AN ADDITIONAL AN' MO' SERIOUS DANGER. CAIN HAS A GUNMAN NAME O' SANDERS ON HIS PAYROLL.

HE NOT ONLY HAS A CERTAIN TALENT, PLUS REMARKABLE SPEED, HE SEEMS TO ENJOY HIS WORK ENORMOUSLY.

STAN LYNDE

© Field Enterprises, Inc. 1981

3/18

I APPRECIATE THE WARNING, DUKE,, AND IT'S BEEN GOOD TO SEE YOU AGAIN. YOU TOO, MISS ASPEN.

LIKEWISE, MARSHAL,, DON'T BE A STRANGER.

I,,I DON'T KNOW WHAT IT IS ABOUT THAT MAN, DUKE,, BUT HE DOES GET TO ME,,

,,IN A WAY NO MAN HAS FOR A LONG, LONG TIME. I THINK I COULD BE SOMETHING TO HIM.

REALLY, DEAR ASPEN? SUCH AS?

SUCH AS,, WHATEVER HE'D WANT ME TO BE.

© Field Enterprises, Inc. 1981

STAN LYNDE

3/19

SO THAT'S THE NEW MARSHAL. FRIEND O' YOURS, BOSS?

YES,, IF AH HAVE A FRIEND, IT IS HIM, JOAB,,

,,AN' AH FEAR THAT HE MAY HAVE SOME DIFFICULTY IN BRINGIN' LAW AN' ORDER TO THIS COMMUNITY.

THEREFO' WE WILL, AS GOOD CITIZENS, GIVE HIM OUR FULL SUPPORT.

THOONK!

STAN LYNDE

© Field Enterprises, Inc. 1981

TWO MAIN **STREETS** IN THIS TOWN,, FRONT STREET AND TRAIL AVENUE,,

,,ONE BANK, FOUR SALOONS, A DANCE HALL, AND AN ABANDONED CHURCH. AND ONE LAWMAN,, ME.

GUESS I'LL HAVE SOME LUNCH WHILE' THINGS ARE QUIET,,I'VE GOT A FEELIN' THEY WON'T **STAY** THAT WAY.

GOLDEN FLEECE **CAFE** J. HARMONY, PROP.

ACE BILLIARD HALL & CARD ROOM

STAN LYNDE

WELCOME TO THE GOLDEN FLEECE CAFE, MARSHAL,, I'M JOHN HARMONY, OWNER, COOK, DISHWASHER, AND HEAD WAITER!

GOOD TO MEET YOU, JOHN,, I'M COLE CANTRELL.

I HEARD YOU WERE IN TOWN,,LORD KNOWS WE SURE DO **NEED** YOU AROUND HERE,,

,,AND AS A FURTHER WELCOME, YOUR LUNCH TODAY IS **FREE**,, WHICH IS JUST ABOUT WHAT IT'S **WORTH**!

STAN LYNDE

THERE YOU GO, MARSHAL,,CHILI AN' A BOTTLE O' BEER, FRESH OFF THE ICE.

THANKS, JOHN,, LOOKS GOOD.

WELL, LOOKY THERE! THERE'S THAT NEW **TOWN TAMER** WE'VE BEEN HEARIN' ABOUT, JED!

YEAH,,HE EVEN **EATS** LIKE A ORDINARY HUMAN,,

,,I WONDER DOES HE **SCARE** LIKE A ORDINARY HUMAN.

STAN LYNDE

THAT NEW MARSHAL DON'T LOOK ALL THAT TOUGH TO ME, CURLY,, WHAT SAY WE **TEST** HIM A LITTLE ?

I,,I DON'T KNOW, JED,,LOOKS CAN BE DECEIVIN',,

,,FIRST SKUNK I SEEN AS A KID I THOUGHT WAS A KITTY CAT,, 'TIL I TRIED T' PET HIM.

WHAT'S THE MATTER WITH YOU? THERE'S **TWO** OF US, AN' ONLY ONE O' HIM!

YEAH,,BUT IF WHAT I HEAR ABOUT HIM IS TRUE, WE STILL COULD BE **OUTNUMBERED.**

STAN LYNDE

61.

OUR OUTFIT,, THE M-CROSS,, SPENDS A GOOD DEAL O' MONEY IN THIS TOWN, ACE,,

,,AN' WE'VE COME TO EXPECT CERTAIN PRIVILEGES IN RETURN,, LIKE PEACE OFFICERS WHO KNOW THEIR PLACE.

I DON'T RECKON WE'D TAKE KINDLY TO ANY JOHN LAW WHO TAKES HIS JOB TOO SERIOUS.

STAN LYNDE

© Field Enterprises, Inc., 1981

WHAT CAN I TELL YOU, BUCK? I DON'T LIKE TOO MUCH LAW IN MY BUSINESS, EITHER,,

,,SOME OF MY GAMES ARE SHADED PRETTY STRONG IN THE HOUSE'S FAVOR,,

,,AN' THE BAR WHISKEY DOES GET WATERED SOME,, TO MAKE IT GO FARTHER,,

,,BUT SO FAR I AIN'T EVEN MET THE NEW MARSHAL, SO I DON'T KNOW WHETHER HE'S FRIEND OR FOE.

STAN LYNDE

© Field Enterprises, Inc., 1981

WELL, SPEAK O' THE DEVIL, BUCK,, LOOK WHO JUST WALKED IN.

EVENIN', GENTLEMEN,, I'M COLE CANTRELL, THE NEW MARSHAL IN TOWN. ARE YOU ACE HYATT?

I SURELY AM, MARSHAL, I OWN THIS PLACE.

THIS HERE'S BUCK CAIN, HIS FAMILY OWNS THE M-CROSS OUTFIT.

HOWDY, MARSHAL,, 'SCUSE ME IF I DON'T SHAKE HANDS,,

,,BUT I DRUTHER WAIT 'TIL I KNOW A MAN BETTER.

STAN LYNDE

© Field Enterprises, Inc. 1981

WELL,, WELCOME T' RIMFIRE, MARSHAL,, WHAT CAN I DO FOR YOU?

THIS IS SORT OF A GET-ACQUAINTED CALL, ACE,,

,,I'D LIKE TO CHECK OUT YOUR WHEEL AND YOUR TABLES,, SEE IF THEY COMPLY WITH THE CITY ORDINANCES.

I SEE. ARE YOU SAYIN' I RUN CROOKED GAMES HERE?

WHY, NO,, AND I DON'T INTEND TO,, UNLESS YOU ARE.

STAN LYNDE

© Field Enterprises, Inc., 1981

GOOD AFTERNOON, GENTLEMEN,, ARE YOU HERE TO SEE ME?

I'M RUFUS CAIN, MARSHAL,,I OWN THE M-CROSS, YOU'VE GOT MY BOY BUCK IN YOUR JAIL.

THAT IS A FACT, MR. CAIN, HE BROKE THE LAW.

AROUND HERE, THE LAW IS WHAT I SAY IT IS, MISTER,,TURN MY BOY LOOSE!

IF YOU DO THAT,,REAL FAST,, YOU CAN RIDE OUT ALIVE. THAT'S THE ONLY OPTION YOU GET.

I UNDERSTAND YOUR CONCERN, MR. CAIN,,BUT I CAN'T RELEASE YOUR SON JUST NOW,,

,,HE'S BEEN CHARGED WITH A CRIME AND HE HAS TO STAND TRIAL. THAT'S THE LAW.

I TOLD YOU, CANTRELL,, IN THESE PARTS, I'M THE LAW,,

,,AND I WANT MY BOY OUT HERE NOW!

YOU'VE GOT GUTS, CANTRELL,,I'LL GIVE YOU THAT. BUT YOU AIN'T GOT ANY CHOICE,,

,,YOU EITHER BACK DOWN AN' TURN MY BOY LOOSE,, OR YOU DIE.

EVERYBODY DIES SOMETIME, MR. CAIN,,

,,AND YOU COULD BE RIGHT ABOUT THIS BEING MY TIME,,

,,BUT IF THAT'S HOW IT TURNS OUT, I PROMISE YOU I WON'T BE GOING ALONE.